PROTECTING THE OCEANS

John Baines

Conserving Our World

Acid Rain
Conserving Rainforests
Waste and Recycling
Conserving the Atmosphere
Protecting Wildlife
The Spread of Deserts
Farming and the Environment
Protecting the Oceans

Series editor: Sue Hadden
Series designer: Ross George

First published in 1990 by
Wayland (Publishers) Ltd
61 Western Road, Hove
East Sussex BN3 1JD, England

British Library Cataloguing in Publication Data
Baines, John D. (John David), *1943–*
Protecting the oceans.
1. Oceans. Effects of man
I. Title II. Series
304.2'8

ISBN 1–85210–827–4

Typeset by Rachel Gibbs, Wayland
Printed in Italy by G. Canale & C.S.p.a., Turin.
Bound in France by A.G.M.

Contents

An amazing world

Looking at the world from above the Pacific Ocean, it is quite reasonable to ask why this planet is called Earth. From this point, 90 per cent of it is water. Even after changing our position to a view over the maximum amount of land, 50 per cent is still water. In fact, the oceans cover 70 per cent of the Earth's surface.

Humans are land-based animals and it is natural that they have devoted most of their energies towards life on the land. The oceans have been neglected. Although there has been a huge growth in research over the last twenty years or so, little is still known about the marine environment in comparison with land-based (terrestrial) environments. What we do know suggests that the oceans warrant a *Guinness Book of Records* all to themselves.

The oceans contain 90 per cent of the Earth's water. If all the land was flattened, it would be covered to a depth of 150 m. Life on Earth originated in the oceans three and a half billion years ago. It was only 450 million years ago that the first land-dwelling creatures evolved. Today the oceans contain the largest, and some say the most intelligent, living creatures — whales. The blue whale can weigh in at 120 tonnes and measure up to 30 m long.

A satellite photograph showing part of the Pacific Ocean west of the southern USA and Central America. When viewed from space, the Earth has a blue colour because of its oceans.

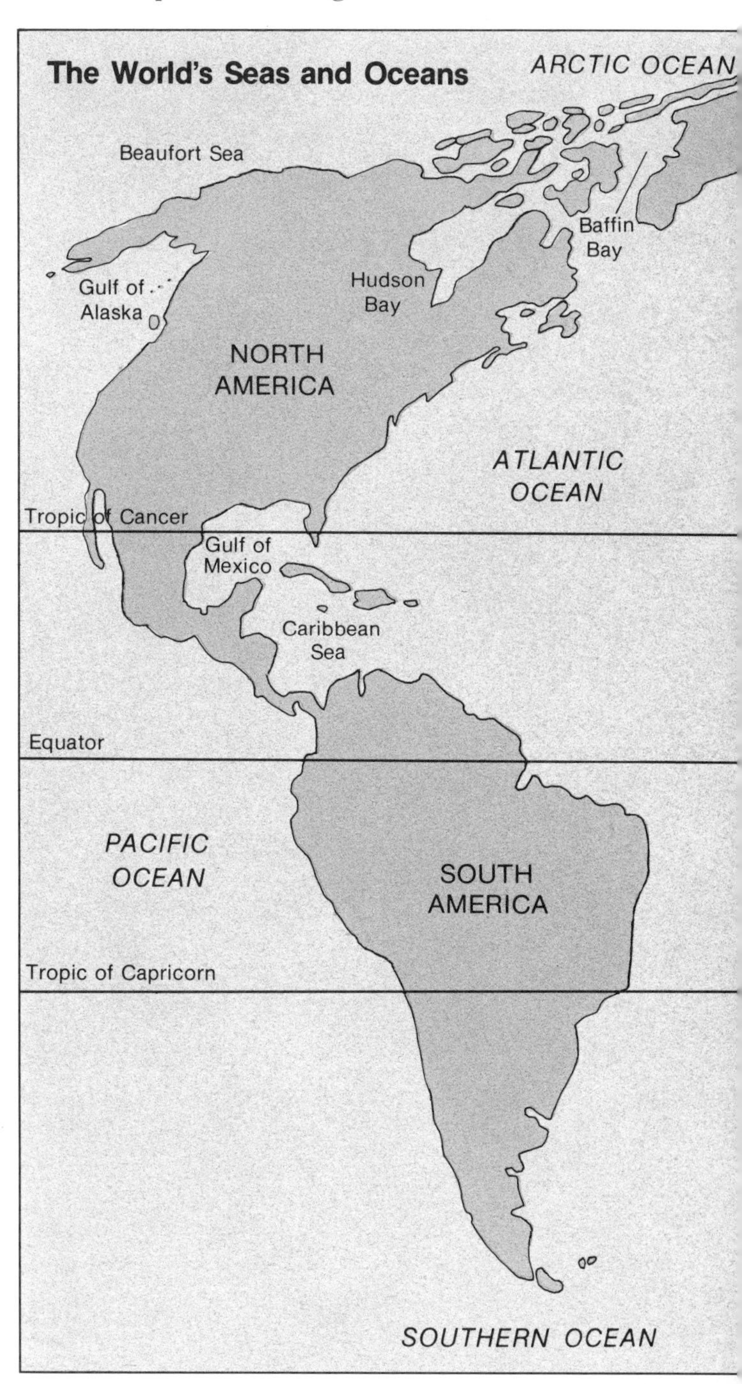

The landscape of the ocean bed is just as impressive. The world's highest mountain, Mount Everest, at 8,840 m above sea level, could easily be lost in the Pacific Ocean's Mariana Trench which is 10,900 m deep. The island of Hawaii represents only the peak of a mountain that rises 9,760 m above the ocean bed. The oceans contain the highest mountains, the deepest gorges and the flattest plains. They have vast sandy beds like our deserts and coral reefs so abundant in life that they resemble our rich tropical rainforests. By contrast, the bottom of the deepest oceans is a cold, dark world where few creatures survive.

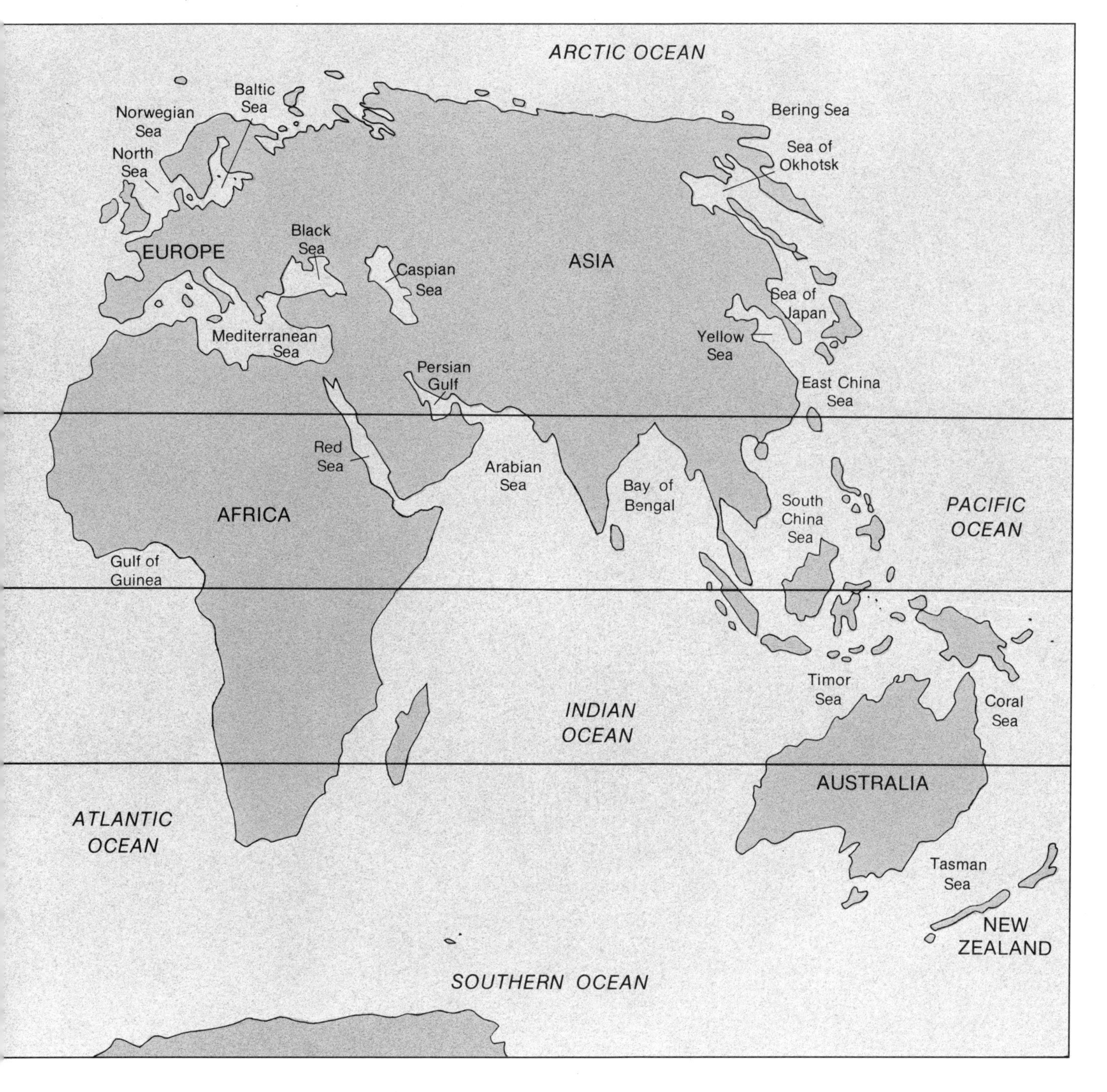

The oceans are a fascinating world, still waiting to be explored and understood. They can provide many resources and humans are not going to leave them alone. In this book we will find out more about the rich life of the oceans. We will look at their usefulness to us and examine the extent to which they have already been damaged by human activities. Finally, we will consider what is being done to control what could become a 'free-for-all' to exploit the valuable ocean resources that either belong to everyone or to no-one, depending on your point of view.

Right *Tropical clown fish live among the poisonous tentacles of sea anemones. Scientists have discovered that these fish are immune to the stinging tentacles, whereas their enemies cannot approach them without being stung by the anemone.*

Opposite *The Hawaiian Islands in the mid Pacific are part of a chain of volcanic mountains that rise almost 10,000 m above the sea-bed.*

Facts and figures

Ocean/Sea	Area (sq km)	Av. depth (m)	Deepest part (m)
Pacific Ocean	165,721,150	4,200	10,860
Atlantic Ocean	81,660,100	3,920	8,385
Indian Ocean	73,444,600	3,962	7,450
Arctic Ocean	14,351,200	1,280	5,334
Mediterranean Sea	2,965,550	1,371	4,593
South China Sea	2,318,000	1,646	5,016
Bering Sea	2,274,000	507	4,090
Caribbean Sea	1,942,500	2,560	7,239
Gulf of Mexico	1,813,000	1,432	3,732
Sea of Okhotsk	1,502,200	914	3,846
East China Sea	1,243,200	185	2,719
Yellow Sea	1,243,200	50	106
Hudson Bay	1,222,500	134	258
Sea of Japan	1,049,000	1,473	4,035
North Sea	572,390	54	659
Red Sea	461,000	454	2,834
Black Sea	436,415	1,310	2,243
Baltic Sea	409,220	67	426

The importance of the oceans

Marine plants and animals

The sea is a huge ecosystem containing thousands of plant and animal species. The most important forms of life in the oceans are tiny algae-like plants called phytoplankton and single-celled animals called zooplankton. These form the basis of the ocean's food chain — without them no other marine creatures could survive. Crabs, starfish, sea anemones, worms and shrimps are just a few of the many small ocean-dwelling animals that feed on plankton.

Right *The oceans contain a huge variety of plant and animal life. All species are put into groups and given Latin names following the Linnaean classification system. This colourful sea slug is called* Flabellinopsis iodinea. *It lives in the world's warmer oceans.*

Above *A manta ray swims gracefully near the ocean surface. These kite-shaped members of the shark family live in the warmer oceans of the world. Some manta rays can measure 6 m across and weigh up to 1.5 tonnes. Despite their size, however, they feed mainly on plankton and small molluscs.*

Species of fish outnumber all other groups of the world's animals. This brightly-coloured file fish ***(opposite)*** *lives among coral reefs in tropical parts of the oceans.*

There are fish of every size and shape: in tropical coastal waters a rich variety of brilliantly-coloured fish, such as butterfly fish and parrot fish, feed on the coral reefs. Further out to sea, swordfish and tuna feed on shoals of smaller fish such as mackerel, herring and sardine. All kinds of sharks live in the world's oceans, from the kite-shaped manta ray to the world's biggest fish, the whale shark. Although it is 18 m long and weighs some 40 tonnes, it is a harmless plankton feeder. At the bottom of the deepest oceans, it is so dark that some fish provide their own light using luminous bacteria that live on them.

With their sleek bodies and flippers, sea lions are well suited to life in the sea. These Californian sea lions are protected in Farallon National Wildlife Refuge, USA.

A number of mammals live in the seas. Whales and dolphins are superbly adapted to saltwater life. Some have teeth for feeding on fish, while others, including the blue whale, feed on plankton. Seals, walruses and sea otters spend most of their lives at sea but, unlike whales and dolphins, must return to land to bear their young.

From the Arctic to the Southern Ocean, different species of seabirds fly above the water, suddenly diving to snatch a fish. The albatross is the world's largest seabird. It patrols the oceans of the Southern Hemisphere for hours at a time, scarcely beating its 3 m-span wings. Puffins are much better swimmers than fliers, while penguins are the best-adapted seabirds of all.

There are even some reptiles that prefer the sea to the land. Several species of sea turtle and sea snake swim gracefully in the world's warmer oceans, returning to land to lay their eggs. In the Galapagos islands, a swimming lizard called the marine iguana dives into the sea to feed on seaweed.

All the plants and animals of the oceans, from the tiny plankton to the huge blue whale, are part of the marine ecosystem. If one species declines or dies out, this will affect all the other species.

All marine life helps to maintain a balanced level of gases, such as oxygen and carbon dioxide, in the atmosphere. Marine plants and animals can also clean up some of the waste that we put into the sea. Scientists are learning more about them so that damage from human activity can be prevented.

Fishing

Humans have fished the seas for centuries. Today, with sophisticated detection and fishing equipment, it is possible to harvest the sea much more efficiently. In 1985, 84 million tonnes of fish were caught around the world, providing much-needed food. With good management, the oceans could provide even more.

Above *Marine iguanas live on the Galapagos Islands in the Pacific Ocean. These islands have always been isolated from the mainland and many unique species have evolved here.*

Below *A colony of erect-crested penguins on the coast of New Zealand. These flightless birds are beautifully adapted to swimming in the sea, where they catch fish.*

Waves and tides

As well as providing an ideal environment for plants and animals to live in, sea water has other valuable properties, one of which is that it moves.

The most obvious signs of these are the waves and the tides. Winds cause the waves, and the gravitational pull of the moon and the sun causes the tides. In places like the Bay of Fundy in Canada, the difference between the high and low tide level can be as much as 12 m.

France has already built a barrage at La Rance in Brittany to use the energy in the tides to generate electricity. Britain too is thinking of building massive barrages across some of its major estuaries, such as the Severn estuary. Waves can generate electricity and some small-scale experiments are taking place to learn more about this. One of the most encouraging areas of research uses the difference in the temperature of sea water at the surface and deep down to generate electricity.

Waves are made by the wind. The longer the stretch of water over which the wind blows, the larger the wave becomes. The energy absorbed by the waves can be used to generate electricity.

Energy from the tides has been harnessed at La Rance tidal barrage in Brittany, France. As the tidal water passes through the sluices of the barrage, it turns turbines which generate electricity.

As the moon orbits the Earth, it pulls part of the ocean surface towards it in an outward bulge. The bulge travels around the world, following the course of the moon. The spinning motion of the Earth creates another bulge, on the opposite side of the world. The bulges cause high tides. The troughs between them cause low tides. As the positions of the sun and moon change during the year, different tides occur. Spring tides occur at full and new moon, while neap tides occur at half moon.

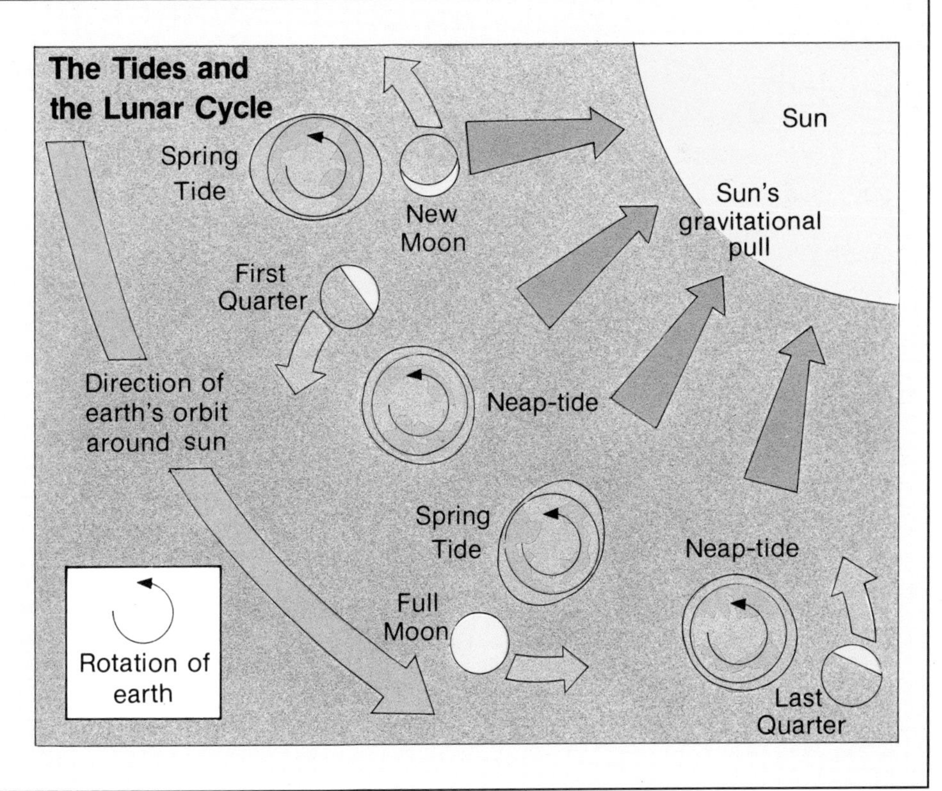

Ocean currents

As the Earth rotates, and as the winds blow, the water of the oceans is moved as currents. These ocean currents carry huge masses of water over long distances, forming a pattern. The North Atlantic Drift transports 55 million cubic metres per second across the Atlantic Ocean towards Europe. That is fifty times more water than is flowing in all the world's rivers! Without it, the climate of north-west Europe would be sub-arctic and much drier. London, for example, is on the same latitude as the mouth of the St. Lawrence River in Canada, where the sea freezes in winter.

The constant circulation of water in the oceans allows nutrients to be moved from one place to another. For example, the cool Peruvian current that moves north along the west coast of South America is particularly rich in plankton. These, in turn, support a huge population of fish. The fish are an important source of food, not only for people, but for millions of sea birds.

Opposite *The ocean floor can provide valuable raw materials, including oil. Offshore drilling rigs have become common in many of the shallow seas, including here off the coast of California, USA.*

Below *A diagram showing the courses of warm and cold currents of the world's oceans.*

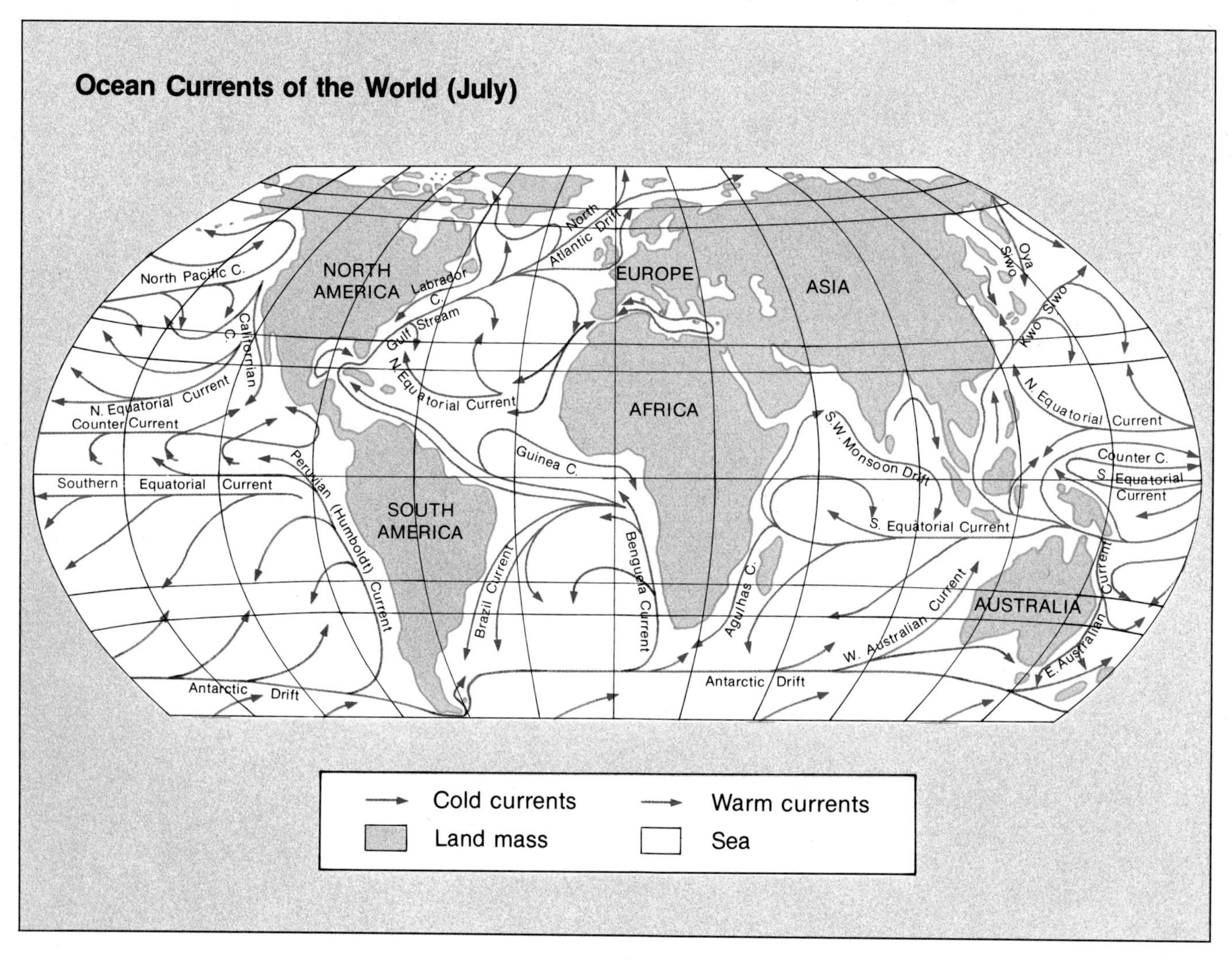

Mineral resources

The oceans contain many minerals that are of use to humans. As resources on the land become scarcer and more expensive, industry is developing ways of using the minerals from the sea. Oil is already pumped from below the sea-bed, and sand and gravel are dredged from the sea-bed. Scientists are still discovering some of the minerals that lie in the world's oceans.

The world's oceans are not just a vast area of water containing abundant life. They govern our rainfall, regulate world temperatures and provide us with a breathable atmosphere. Without these vital 'services' the Earth would not be habitable. The oceans can also process certain amounts of waste and make it safe, provided they are not overloaded. But they are not an inexhaustible resource; they can be damaged. As we plan how to make use of the oceans, we must make sure that they are not harmed, because in the end we will only harm ourselves.

Pollution and the oceans

THE SOURCES OF POLLUTION

'There is no mystery to marine pollution. The worst problem today is the huge quantity of raw sewage and industrial effluent spewed into the sea with no thought for the consequences.'

This was said by Stjepan Kecknes, Director of the Oceans and Coastal Areas Programme Activity Centre run by UNEP (United Nations Environment Programme). Its task is to help clean up the world's seas. Eighty five per cent of the 20 billion tonnes of pollution put into the oceans annually comes from the land. Ninety per cent of that pollution stays in the coastal area, causing serious environmental and health problems. In this chapter, we will find out how the seas become polluted and what damage is caused.

Human sewage

All over the world, vast amounts of human sewage are poured into the sea. Some of it is treated, some in a raw state. The oxygen and bacteria in the sea are very efficient at breaking down sewage, making it safe and recycling it for use by plants and animals. After all, the sea is full of animals producing sewage all the time. However, there are limits to how much can be put in.

The number of people living in coastal cities is increasing worldwide and more sewage is produced than the sea can cope with. Technically, treating the sewage before it is put into the sea is no problem, but it costs money. Developing countries, in particular, lack the

About 50 million litres of raw sewage are put into the Pacific Ocean daily from this pipe at Moa Point, near Wellington, New Zealand. It is next to a popular surfing beach.

Waste from a phosphate fertilizer works in Togo, west Africa, is pumped directly into the sea. This is a cheap method of disposal but how much can the sea take before it starts to suffer?

financial resources to build sufficient sewage treatment plants. Some of the worst problems are in South-east Asia, where there are few treatment plants. Even in rich countries, there is often a reluctance to spend money on treatment plants, and so human sewage regularly turns up on popular bathing beaches. This is not just unpleasant; it is a health hazard.

Industrial and urban waste

Many of the world's cities support a large population and heavy industry. Vast quantities of industrial waste are either dumped into the sea or find their way into it along the rivers into which it is pumped. Whereas human waste is organic and can be recycled by the sea, much industrial waste is inorganic and does not break down so easily, if at all. It gradually builds up, causing more and more pollution. Over 100,000 different chemicals find their way into the sea and often no-one knows what the consequences will be. Most stay in the coastal areas, but because the sea is one huge moving system, the chemicals are gradually transported into all the oceans. No-one knows how all the chemicals affect the creatures that live in oceans.

Not all the waste comes from industry. Much of it comes from household chemicals that are washed down the drain. Rainwater also washes oil, grease and other dirt from roads, vehicles and buildings into the drains. Rain falling into the sea is also contaminated with air-borne pollution from factory chimneys, central heating units and vehicle exhausts.

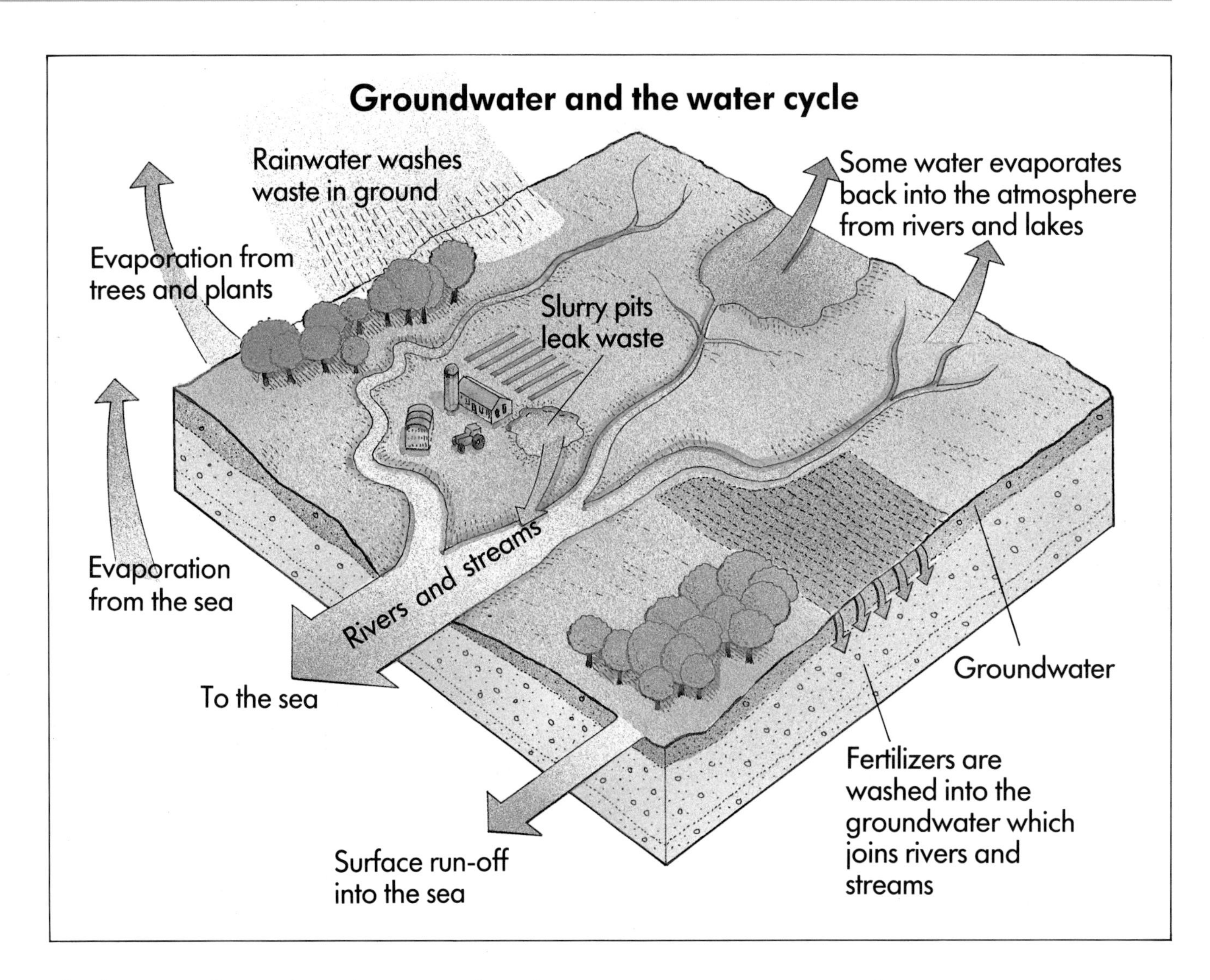

The diagram ***above*** *shows how agricultural waste passes into streams and rivers, eventually finding its way to the sea.*

Agricultural waste

Some of the chemicals used in farming also end up in the sea. Fertilizers are put on the land to make crops grow better; insecticides are widely used by farmers to kill insects that could damage the crops; and herbicides are sprayed on crops to kill unwanted weeds. Some of these strong chemicals run into the streams and rivers and from there into the sea, where they can continue to be active and cause damage, for example an abnormal growth of algae.

Oil

It is estimated that about six million tonnes of oil gets into the sea every year. Almost half a million are the result of shipping accidents. The remainder comes from tankers which wash out their tanks with sea water and illegally dump it into the sea, oil refineries, the terminals where tankers load and unload, drilling rigs in the ocean and undersea oil pipelines. Some is washed off the roads, cars and buildings by the rain and runs into the sea.

Waste disposal

Waste is also loaded in ships and dumped at sea. Sewage sludge from England is regularly dumped at a special site in the North Sea. Hazardous waste from industry, for example PCBs used in the electrical industry, are burnt at sea in special incineration ships. Many ports are only kept open by dredgers removing silt from the river bed and dumping it out at sea. This silt can be heavily contaminated with the waste products of the towns and industry surrounding the port.

People are now much more careful about what they dump in the sea than before. At the end of the Second World War, 170,000 tonnes of poisonous gases were put into ships and the ships scuttled in Norwegian fjords. The authorities are now trying to trace and recover the containers before they start to leak and damage local fishing grounds.

Rubbish dumped on a beach on Lanzarote that is also used by breeding turtles. If wildlife is not to suffer further damage, people must dispose of their waste safely.

Radioactive waste

Radioactive waste needs very special treatment because it can cause cancers and alter how living things grow. Some needs to be kept safe for thousands of years. The sea was once considered the perfect disposal ground and drums of waste were dropped into the deep ocean, where no-one would be harmed. This practice has now been stopped.

The Irish Sea is affected in a different way. Water containing small amounts of radioactive material from the nuclear reprocessing plant at Sellafield is sent down a pipe into the Irish Sea. It is the world's most radioactive sea as a result. The Irish government is pressing for the closure of the reprocessing plant because it says the increased radiation in the sea is to blame for higher-than-normal rates of cancer in some coastal communities. Recently, large bubbles of air breaking at the surface were found to contain plutonium which has come from Sellafield. The air bubble brings the plutonium from the bed of the sea into the atmosphere, where it can be blown on to the land.

The environmental group Greenpeace barrassed ships dumping radioactive waste in the sea in 1982. This generated much publicity and led to such dumping being banned.

Some oil gets into the oceans following accidents. Then it is often washed up on beaches as black, sticky tar. This is unpleasant for humans and dangerous to wildlife.

The effects of pollution

The seaside and the beach are places to which many people like to go to enjoy a holiday or just a day out. Many towns along the coast make their living from the visitors and they therefore depend upon the sea and the beaches being clean and safe. New Brighton at the mouth of the River Mersey in England was one such town, but now its beach is so polluted with sewage and industrial waste, that holiday makers do not go there. Forty per cent of Britain's most popular beaches fall below the recommended standards laid down by the European Community. The main problem is human sewage, but on many beaches, holiday makers have to pick their way through black, sticky oil, broken glass and other debris that has been washed up. Pollution is causing the sea off the north coast of West Germany to get whipped up into a sticky foam.

Above *Some dogs enjoying a splash in the sea. However, dogs foul beaches and therefore many people feel they should not be allowed in bathing areas. In many seaside towns, such as Brighton, England, the local authority prohibits dogs from going on the beach* ***(right)***.

Pollution is also dangerous. Sewage is a health hazard and swimming in polluted water causes unpleasant ailments such as gastroenteritis, skin irritations and ear, nose and throat infections. A research programme in the USA found that, on average, eighteen out of every thousand people swimming in polluted water became ill. Many bathing beaches in the Mediterranean, including Valencia, Barcelona and Marseilles are at the limit of acceptable pollution. Naturally, the pollution is not widely publicized in case the tourists are put off. Australia's famous Bondi beach is still popular with surfers although many of them catch ear infections or suffer an upset stomach due to the sewage pollution. In the summer of 1988, many beaches around New York had to be closed because dangerous hospital waste was being washed up on them. The waste included infected syringes that could injure bare-footed bathers.

At Bournemouth beach, England, regular seawater samples are taken by the local water authority to be quality-tested in a laboratory.

Pollution and marine life

In South-east Asia, it is estimated that one quarter of the people living at or near the coast make their living from the sea. Their waters are also some of the worst polluted by sewage. Shellfish like mussels and oysters are among the first to be seriously affected. In many places around the world, they are not safe to eat. The Mediterranean was famous for its variety of seafood, including shellfish, but now only 4 per cent of the recognized growing areas are considered safe resources. Twenty thousand people poured into the hospitals of Shanghai after eating clams from a polluted area, and when three people died after eating mussels from Prince Edward Island in Canada, the industry and the livelihood of many people virtually collapsed.

Industrial pollution has contaminated some areas where gathering shellfish was once a way of life. This notice ***(above)*** *is beside a chemicals factory in north-east England.*

Dolphins that swim by Monkey Mia beach, Australia, appear not to mind the attention of bathers. How sad it would be if such wonderful experiences shared by people and animals were to disappear as a result of pollution.

Most species are able to tolerate a certain amount of pollution, but with 20 billion tonnes of waste ending up in the sea each year, it is not surprising that marine life is suffering. Most goes unreported, but sometimes the disasters are on such a scale, that they cannot be ignored. During 1988, 80 per cent of the common seals in the North Sea died with a virus. Although it is not known whether pollution directly caused their deaths, research has shown that PCBs reduce an animal's ability to resist disease. PCBs were found in most of the dead seals.

Opposite *Seafood is a nutritious and popular food in most parts of the world. If it is to remain safe to eat, the seas must be kept clean.*

Other species are also suffering. Over the last forty years several species of whales and dolphins (cetaceans) have reduced dramatically in number in the waters around Europe. The University of Oxford in England has established a programme to count the number of occasions on which cetaceans are spotted and has found evidence that they are declining in the most polluted areas.

'I can't believe it's a coincidence that the areas in which the harbour porpoise and bottlenose dolphin are most in decline — the southern North Sea and the English Channel — are also amongst the most polluted seaways in the world'.

Dr. Peter Evans,
Oxford University
cetacean research unit.

These Jackass penguins were harmed by an oil spill. They are being cleaned with a chemical solution derived from oil.

Oil pollution

When oil is spilt into the ocean it makes a slick. This is dangerous to those animals that use the surface of the ocean like birds, seals and whales. Oil spills also devastate coastlines. In 1980, 50,000 seabirds died on the Skaggerak between Denmark and Sweden as a result of one oil spill. The oil coats their wings and prevents them from flying. When the birds try to preen their feathers to remove the oil, it poisons them. A few are rescued and cleaned before being returned to the wild. Once the sea is clean, populations are able to recover within a few years, but the sight of so much suffering is very upsetting.

PCBs and the environment

Polychlorinated biphenyls (PCBs) are complex chemicals that are used in the electrical industry. They are extremely dangerous if they get into the environment, and as a result their use is being phased out. However, they have found their way into the marine environment and are now found in the bodies of many animals. Five and a half tonnes of PCBs in electrical equipment on the oil drilling rig Piper Alpha may now be in the North Sea after the terrible disaster in July 1988 which destroyed it. When they are taken in by an animal, PCBs do not pass through but build up in the body. At each higher level in the food chain, the PCBs become more concentrated.

PCBs can reduce the body's resistance to disease, reduce the learning ability of children, damage the central nervous system, cause cancer and affect babies in the womb. Because of the dangers to people, New York State is spending 27 million dollars to clean up a 12 km stretch of the Hudson River where the bed has become contaminated with PCBs.

PCBs can be sent to special treatment plants where they are burnt at very high temperatures. However, the treatment of PCBs is a controversial issue. In August 1989 several ports in England refused to unload containers of PCB waste that had been sent from Canada for treatment. The ship carrying them had to return to Canada.

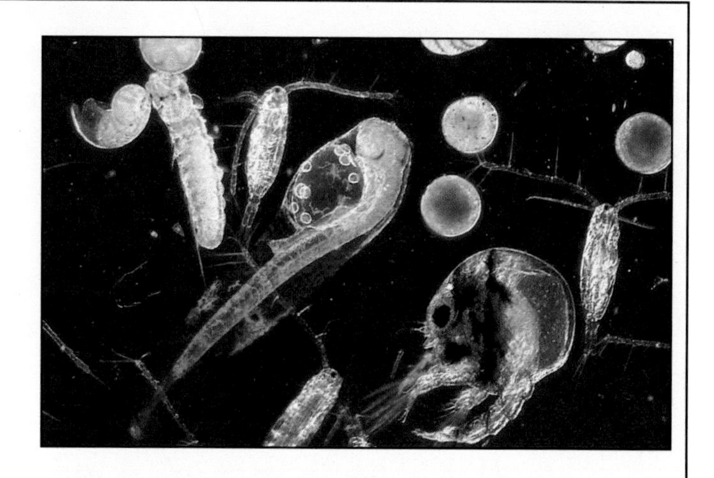

Plankton is the basis of many food chains. If it is damaged by pollution, the effects can extend to the top of the food chain.

Oil slick in the Last Wilderness

On 23 March 1989 the tanker Exxon Valdez set off from the port of Valdez in Alaska carrying millions of litres of oil drilled from Alaskan oil fields. As the tanker made its way through Prince William Sound, it hit jagged rocks on Bligh Reef. Ten holes were pierced in the tanker's hull and immediately oil began to leak from them.

Over the next few days 44 million litres of oil leaked into the Sound, creating a huge oil slick — the worst in American history. Local oil workers were not prepared for such a disaster and by the time they managed to contain the slick with booms and skimmers, most of the damage had been done. A 1200 km stretch of Alaska's coastline was polluted with oil. Thousands of ducks and seabirds were killed as oil clogged their feathers; many sea otters suffocated in the oil slick. Bald eagles and brown bears were also affected as they scavenged food from the oiled beaches. The oil poisoned countless fish and crabs, threatening the livelihood of many Alaskan fishermen.

Since the disaster, the oil company Exxon has employed many local Alaskan people to clean the worst of the oil from the beaches. However, it will take many years for all traces of the oil to disappear from the area.

The Exxon Valdez disaster has increased international concern over the development of the Alaskan oil fields. Alaska is widely regarded as America's last wilderness and many people feel it should be preserved as a wildlife haven. However, the oil industry provides 85 per cent of Alaska's revenue. Alaskan oil also provides a quarter of all the oil used in the USA.

Cleaning an oiled Alaskan beach, April 1989.

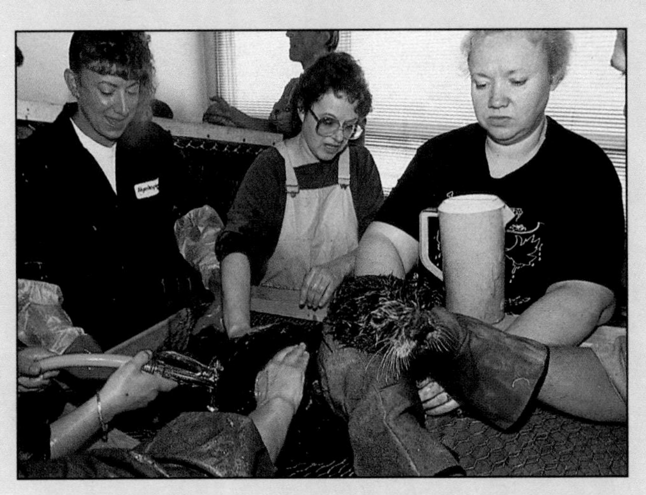

Many sea otters died after the Exxon Valdez disaster. Some were saved by volunteers.

The controversy over Alaskan oil production will continue. Meanwhile, the local people cannot forget the devastation they have seen:

'People are going to have strong feelings about this for a long time. Every time they go to a favourite fishing hole, they will think of the spill and they will be angry.'

Dennis Kelso
Alaskan State environmental minister.

Cleaning up oil pollution at sea — what can be done?

The crash of the Exxon tanker Valdez near the coast of Alaska in March 1989, has shown how much the environment can be damaged by oil spills. What can be done to clean up oil spills at sea?

1) ***Leave it:*** *If the oil spill is a long way from land, it is often best to leave it and allow it to break up naturally. It will eventually disappear into the air and water, although the residue may turn up on a coastline months or years later as a sticky tar ball.*

2) ***Dispersants:*** *Strong detergents can be sprayed on to the oil and break it up more quickly. However, they cannot be used close to the land as the chemicals are poisonous and can contaminate or kill marine life.*

Detergents used to clear oil spills can also pollute the environment, as here in Cornwall after the Torrey Canyon *oil disaster in March 1967.*

Following an oil spill in California, USA, red booms were placed on the water to contain the oil, so preventing it from reaching the shore.

3) **Sinking:** Oil floats on the surface, but it can be made to sink by spreading powdered chalk on it. The powder soaks up the oil and sinks. While this clears the surface quickly, the oil only ends up on the sea-bed, where it can continue to damage those plants and animals living there.

4) **Absorption:** Several materials such as straw, peat and polystyrene can absorb oil when spread on it. The oily mixture can then be collected and disposed of safely. This method is good because it removes the oil, but it can only be used in calm conditions and if the spill is not too large.

5) **Booms:** Floating barriers can be placed in the water which contain the movement of the oil. These are known as booms. They can stop it reaching a sensitive area, such as a popular beach or a wildlife area. If the slick is not too big, they can be placed all around the oil. A tanker then sucks up the oil from the surface. Once again, calm water is needed for this method to be successful.

Removing the oil from the sea is the best environmental option, but it is not always possible. The oil must be contained very rapidly, otherwise it will spread too far for any effective action to be taken.

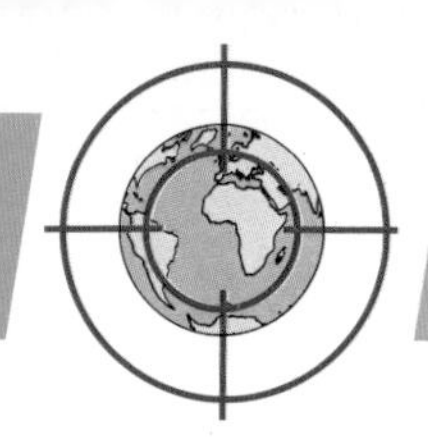

Mining and the oceans

Every day resources are used. The list of them is very long. Coal and oil provide energy; bauxite, iron, copper and other ores are used for making metals; limestone and chalk are used for cement; timber is used for furniture and buildings, and so on. Many of the resources used are not renewable — once used they are gone for ever. Oil, for example, is a non-renewable resource and experts estimate that our oil reserves will last for between forty and sixty years. As the major sources of raw materials on the land are depleted, the raw materials found in the ocean are being explored and exploited.

Minerals from the sea?

The oceans are very rich in mineral resources. The sea water itself contains over seventy elements. Every cubic kilometre contains 230 million tonnes of salt. Other minerals are found in much smaller quantities, including magnesium, iron and gold. Most are in such small quantities that it is uneconomic to recover them, although Japan intends to recover uranium from the sea for its nuclear energy programme.

In places, the sea-bed itself is covered in mineral-rich deposits. Vast areas are covered in pear-shaped nodules that contain 25 per cent manganese. At depths of 5,000 m, they are expensive but not impossible to mine. The Red Sea has deposits of copper, silver and zinc which are found in the silt lying on the bottom. These could be more easily recovered.

Our industrial society depends upon oil for energy. Crude oil is processed at refineries, like this one in New Jersey, USA, and turned into products such as petrol.

Land is being reclaimed in Bahrain by dredging material from the sea bed and dumping it to make a causeway.

Drilling rigs are a familiar sight in the world's oceans. This rig is in the South China Sea.

The sea-bed is already mined in some places. Around the coast of Britain, about 16 million tonnes of sand and gravel are dredged from the sea every year. The Thames Barrier, which was built to protect London from flooding, contains over 400,000 tonnes of sand and gravel taken from the North Sea. Using resources from the sea-bed can save environments on the land, but it is also important to be sure that the environment of the sea is not badly damaged.

The continents extend beneath the sea as the continental shelf. The rocks contain resources just as they do on the land. Mining offshore for oil is already taking place in several areas including the North Sea, the Gulf of Mexico and the Persian Gulf. Many other ocean areas are being explored. Great care is taken to avoid accidents, as the damage to the marine environment could be very serious.

The Antarctic

The Southern Ocean lies around the continent of Antarctica and numerous small groups of islands, such as the Falklands (or Malvinas, as they are also called). Although it is known that the continent and the ocean contain many valuable minerals, there has been little development as yet because of the Antarctic Treaty.

The Treaty first came into effect in 1959. It is signed by sixteen countries who are responsible for managing Antarctica for peaceful purposes. These countries help to organize research into the Antarctic environment. It was this research that first discovered the damage to the Earth's ozone layer from the use of CFCs (chlorofluorocarbons).

In 1982, the Convention on the Conservation of Antarctic Marine Living Resources was developed as a means of researching and managing krill. These are small shrimp-like creatures that swarm in huge quantities in the Southern Ocean. If they were caught commercially, they could double the annual catch of seafood to around 160 million tonnes per year. However, they are also the source of food for five species of whale, as well as seals, birds and fish. It is therefore important to find out how many tonnes can be caught without the whales and other species starving.

Tiny krill swarm in the southern oceans and could become an important source of food for humans and farm animals. But what effect would harvesting krill have on the sea creatures that depend on them?

Hunting and fishing

The North Sea herring fishing industry

The North Sea used to provide over 4 million tonnes of herring a year. Small fishing fleets from villages and towns all along the coast made a good living from them. Herring was a cheap but very nutritious food.

By 1975, larger fleets using more expensive equipment had taken most of the fish and the catch was reduced to almost zero. To save the herring from extinction in the North Sea, and to allow stocks to build up again, herring fishing was stopped. This will help the herring, but it has ruined the livelihoods of many small fishing communities. If the fishing had been managed properly, the herring could have continued to provide food and employment for as long as was needed.

Similar stories could be written about the pilchards of the south-west coast of Africa, anchovies off the coast of Peru and sardines off the coast of California.

Modern fishing techniques result in huge hauls of fish. However, unless fishing is carefully controlled, certain fish species could decline to danger point.

Overfishing

The oceans of the world provide over 80 million tonnes of fish a year. Fish are important food in many countries, although one third of all fish caught are fed to animals or used as fertilizer on the land.

Unlike some species of freshwater fish, such as trout, fish from the sea are not farmed; they are hunted. Fishermen have to find areas rich in fish and then try to catch them. It is an activity that has gone on for thousands of years and could continue for thousands more, as long as we do not become too greedy.

Many countries have set up a 200-mile (320 km) Exclusive Economic Zone around their coasts, in which they can control fishing. However control beyond the limit is less easy, and the deep sea fleets of the richer nations, like Japan and the Soviet Union, are systematically 'emptying' the sea of its fish. Using modern equipment they can take a huge haul at one time.

In theory, the oceans could supply up to 100 million tonnes of fish a year for ever, but only if enough are left to breed. Today very fine nets are stretched over hundreds of kilometres at a time, catching all kinds of sea creatures, whether wanted or not.

These fishermen in the Sultanate of Oman are removing sardines from their nets. Local fishermen often find their livelihoods ruined when fleets from other countries take too many fish.

Fishing casualties

Tuna fish swim beneath and behind large schools of dolphins. When fishing crews see the dolphins, they know the tuna are likely to be there as well. They surround the area with nets, and pull them into a tighter and tighter circle. The dolphins as well as the tuna are caught. Unable to reach the surface to breathe, the dolphins drown. Every year about 100,000 dolphins are killed in this way off the coast that stretches from California to Chile in South America. About 3,000 porpoises die each year in the North Sea when they get caught in fishing nets. A member of the crew of Greenpeace's 'Rainbow Warrior' described the plight of one of them:

'The porpoise must have put up a terrific struggle before she drowned. Her body was entangled in five layers of mono-filament net of the type that Japanese fishermen stretch hundreds of kilometres across the ocean at a time'.

Marine mammals such as dolphins and seals are not only killed accidentally. They are regularly culled by fishermen to 'protect' their fish stocks. While the fishermen claim that these mammals feed on their fish stocks, it is overfishing by humans that is usually the most serious cause of stocks declining.

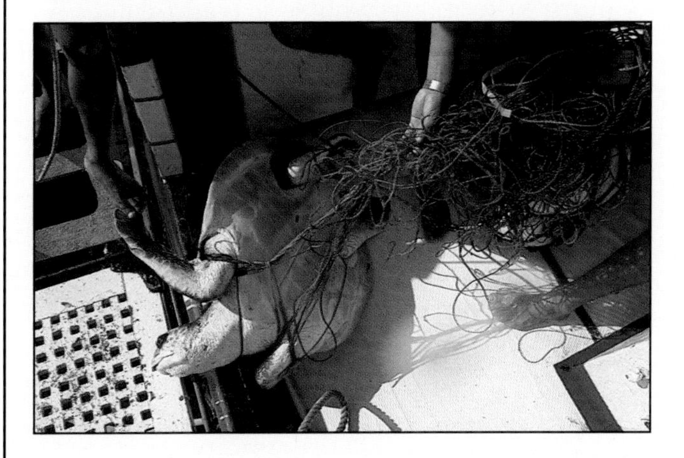

A turtle is freed from a fishing net. Many other trapped victims are less fortunate.

A huge fin whale is cut up and processed in Iceland. This photograph was taken before a total ban on whaling was agreed by the International Whaling Commission.

Whales and whaling

During the autumn of 1988, three grey whales became trapped under the ice off the coast of Alaska and were unable to migrate south. The media around the world broadcast their plight, as the whales banged against the ice to try and break it and reach the air they needed. Weakened and scarred by their efforts, they seemed doomed to die until an international rescue operation was launched.

Thousands of dollars were spent on keeping holes open for them, while a channel was cut to the open sea. Finally, the whales were directed to safety, by playing whale sounds at the end of the channel. What unusual behaviour from the human species which, over the last hundred years, has hunted many species of whales to the verge of extinction without thought for their welfare!

The hunting of whales probably generates more concern and debate than that of any other wild creature. 'Save the Whale' was one of the first environmental campaigns and one of the most successful, as it has led to a ban on all commercial whaling.

The International Whaling Commission

Commercial whaling developed on a major scale in the last century. As one species was hunted almost to extinction, another one was chosen to take its place. The outlook for the survival of many species was bleak. In 1946 the International Whaling Commission was established to try and regulate the whaling industry. It failed because there was no scientific data from which to tell a country how many whales it could catch. As a result, quotas were not kept and the stocks continued to decline. By the 1970s there was a widespread public concern for the future of whales and more non-whaling countries joined the Commission. With better scientific evidence to support the anti-whaling case, a moratorium (ban) on all commercial whaling was agreed from 1985. Japan and the Soviet Union, however, have objected to this and still catch some whales.

Conservation as a moral issue

For many people, whaling is not a commercial or straightforward conservation issue. It is a moral one. Whales are very intelligent and sensitive creatures; they use a complex communications system and show great care and concern for each other. They live in almost total harmony with their ocean environment. Why should they have to endure the pain and suffering inflicted on them by a harpoon gun to provide meat and other products for which perfectly acceptable substitutes have been developed?

A sperm whale is harpooned. Scientific evidence in 1989 showed that whale populations are lower than previously thought. Therefore it is even more important to protect these mammals.

Who owns a whale or a fish?

In coastal waters, the 'ownership' of whales or fish changes as they move from one country's area to another. Agreements can be made to prevent any one country from taking more than its fair share, so depleting stocks. In the deep seas, there are no such agreements and countries have opposing views.

View 1: *In the open seas, the creatures do not belong to anyone. Once caught, they become the property of the catcher who can keep any profit they make as a result of selling their catch.*

View 2: *In the open seas, the creatures belong to everyone. Once caught, everyone should have a share of the profit made from selling them. Everyone also has a right to have a say in the numbers that should be caught.*

Which view do you agree with, or do you have a different view?

The annual slaughter of thousands of pilot whales in the Faroe Islands was publicized by a conservation group called the Environmental Investigation Agency. The Agency has persuaded some Faroese people to stop this cruel tradition.

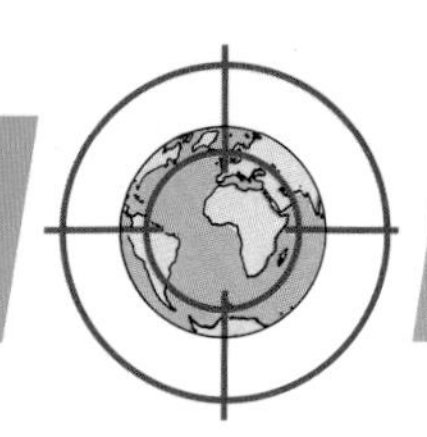

Coastal and marine nature reserves

Marine nature reserves

On the land, many areas have been set aside as nature reserves or national parks to protect special areas. So far, very few marine reserves have been established, although much of the Southern Ocean around Antarctica is protected by the Antarctic Treaty. The largest marine reserve is the Great Barrier Reef. Another important reserve is the Waddenzee in the Netherlands.

Many countries are now realizing the need to set up marine reserves within their territorial waters. However, such reserves can only be successful if they can be protected from pollution, as well as development. This will require activities on the land and at sea to be controlled, which is very difficult.

Marine reserves are unique because they protect such a wide variety of wildlife – not only sea creatures but also seabirds and the unusual plants and animals that thrive on the seashore.

In southern France, the Camargue has been declared a nature reserve, in order to protect its unique wildlife, which includes wild horses and flamingos.

Some of the richest ecosystems are where the sea and the land meet. These areas are able to support a greater variety of species and larger populations of plants and animals than elsewhere. Many species of fish found in the oceans spend part of their lives in these coastal areas and many birds depend on the food they find there. These creatures are also the most threatened of the marine ecosystems.

There are four coastal habitats of particular value to wildlife. They are:

River estuaries

The tidal part of the river near the sea is called the estuary. Rivers carry nutrients from the land into the sea and, as a result, the estuaries teem with life and are good feeding grounds for birds. If you are able to visit an estuary at low tide, you should see a wide variety of wading birds feeding on the exposed mud flats.

In some places, the rivers also carry pollution from sewage works, towns, industries and agriculture. Some rivers and estuaries have become so badly polluted that they support very little marine life.

Salt marshes

Along the shore, especially around the mouths of rivers, are flat muddy areas over which the tide ebbs and flows. They are excellent for wildlife, and birds can often be seen feeding there. The areas furthest from the sea often have plants growing which trap the silt held in the water. The silts build up until the land eventually only gets covered at very high tides and more types of plant become established. These areas are very fertile when drained and protected from the sea. Many have been reclaimed for agriculture or for building and their wildlife value is lost.

Above *The attractive flowers of sea lavender add colour to coasts and salt marshes.*

Left *Many species of birds are attracted to estuaries, including swans and many kinds of ducks.*

The mudskipper is an amphibious fish that is found only in mangrove swamps.

Tourists can walk around the Florida Everglades reserve to see its wide variety of birds, including the anhinga, a type of cormorant.

Mangrove swamps

These are the equivalent of salt marshes in tropical countries. Mangrove swamps occur around the coast of Africa, India, Southeast Asia, South America and also on the coast of Florida, USA. Mangroves are often densely wooded with trees whose roots make an impenetrable tangled mass. They protect the coast from erosion as well as providing a habitat for many types of fish, shellfish and birds. Unusual animals such as ghost and fiddler crabs and mudskippers are found in mangroves.

Large areas have been cleared for coastal developments or for their timber. They too can be damaged by pollution. However, some mangroves are now protected. An example is the Florida Everglades reserve, USA.

Coral reefs

Coral reefs are built of small creatures called polyps which thrive in shallow, clear and clean tropical seas. Some reefs fringe the coast; others are found some distance from the coast. They represent one of the oldest and richest ecosystems on earth, but they too can be damaged by pollution. They are also threatened by mining, as the skeletons of the polyps are made of limestone which is used in the manufacture of cement. The beautiful corals are also collected in some countries to be sold to tourists as souvenirs.

The Great Barrier Reef

The most famous of all the world's coral reefs is the Great Barrier Reef which stretches for 2,000 km along the east coast of Australia, sometimes up to 250 km from the coast. Captain Cook, who was the first person to bring news of the reef's existence to Europe, described it as 'a wall or rock, rising perpendicular out of the unfathomable ocean'. The reef is not just important for its coral but for the marvellous variety of tropical fish and other sea creatures that depend on it.

The Great Barrier Reef has remained one of the great wonders of the world in spite of attempts to prospect for oil along it and to mine the limestone. It now enjoys much greater protection since it has been designated a World Heritage Site. This will protect it from direct exploitation, but it does not protect it from other hazards including pollution and silt from the coast, shipwrecks, the concentrated attention of thousands of tourists and the huge appetite of the starfish called the 'crown of thorns'. Scientists are unwilling to do anything about the starfish, which has eaten so much of the coral, fearing what may happen to the ecology of the reef if they interfere. Their 'cure' could turn out to be worse than the 'disease'.

Above *A blue-streak butterfly fish grazes the coral of the Great Barrier Reef.*

Left *A sea snake swims in Australia's Coral Sea.*

How can we protect the oceans?

Protection from pollution

Protecting the oceans requires action against the three main causes of damage: pollution from sewage, oil, and industrial and agricultural waste; overfishing; and damage to marine and coastal habitats caused by coastal and offshore developments. Before these problems can be effectively tackled, detailed information about the marine environment and how it works is needed. Many countries are now engaged in research to provide this type of information.

Research

The United Nations Environment Programme (UNEP) is the main international organization working to protect and improve the environment as a whole. It has set up the Global Environmental Monitoring System (GEMS) to provide information about the environment. As yet, GEMS does not monitor the oceans adequately, but is aiming to do so during the 1990s. It will help people to understand the marine environment more fully. By monitoring what effect human activities are having on the seas, it should be possible to manage them better.

Above *Ships serve as laboratories for scientists who are finding out more about the oceans and the effects human activities are having on them.*

Left *A wildlife researcher studies a green turtle laying its eggs on Heron Island on the Great Barrier Reef.*

Mussel watch

Mussels are shellfish which are very effective indicators of marine pollution. This is because many of the pollutants become concentrated in their bodies. They do not move and, therefore, show how much pollution there is at that location, unlike fish which move around freely. They are also easy to collect. They can provide a useful indication of the well-being of the marine environment as a whole and give an early warning of any problems. Marine laboratories have been established at many places to collect and examine mussels regularly as part of a global 'mussel watch' scheme. The amounts of pollutants are measured and the results can show which areas need cleaning up and how effective the clean-up operation has been.

The priorities in marine pollution

In 1982, the Joint Group of Experts on the Scientific Aspects of Marine Pollution (GESAMP), sponsored by UNEP, identified the main areas of concern. They included public health risks from sewage and radioactive wastes, the effects of poisonous chemicals and heavy metals on humans, and the disturbance of natural habitats from energy production and ocean bed mining.

UNEP Regional Seas Programme

One country can suffer from marine pollution caused by another, as the ocean currents move the pollution around. To solve the problems, countries must work together and share the costs of improving their coastal waters. The Regional Seas Programme brings together groups of countries that share a particular ocean and helps them to solve pollution problems. The first Action Plan, developed by Mediterranean countries in 1975, is working well. Today there are ten programmes and each area has developed its own Action Plan.

The Programme does not cover all countries, although some regional seas are covered by other agreements. For example, countries bordering the North Sea meet regularly and have reached agreements on fishing, oil pollution and the burning of industrial waste at sea.

Oil pollution

Ships are also responsible for polluting the seas. In 1973, agreement was reached at an international level, including various restrictions on ships dumping waste or cleaning out oil tanks at sea. One way of identifying oil tankers that pollute the sea is to add an identification chemical to the oil. If an oil slick is found, it is then easy to tell which ship caused it. Britain also has a maritime patrol aircraft which looks out for new cases of oil pollution in British waters.

Preventing overfishing

If the seas are to continue to provide a reliable supply of food, then they must not be overfished. This will only happen if all the countries involved in fishing can agree on restrictions governing how much they can catch. Each country could have a quota, stating that it may catch a certain tonnage of fish. Different countries could all agree to use only a certain size of fishing net that allows young fish to swim through. Reaching agreement is difficult unless there is scientific evidence to show that the restrictions are needed. This information is provided by a number of commissions and advisory bodies. One of the best known of these is the International Whaling Commission, which decided to ban all commercial whaling for five years from the end of 1985.

Bathers enjoy a swim on Australia's Bondi beach. Keeping the oceans clean will ensure that they remain safe for us to enjoy in future.

Dividing up the seas

Much of human history has been dominated by wars for the control of territory. Until the twentieth century, a country was allowed to control the sea up to three miles (4.8 km) out from the coast, the three-mile limit. Beyond that, the sea belonged to no country and anyone had the right to travel, fish, hunt or mine there. Almost all of the sea was uncontrolled.

This was leading to a 'free-for-all' and the living resources of the sea, like fish and whales, were declining in numbers. Unwanted waste was being dumped, so creating potential dangers in the future. Some nations were wanting to mine minerals under the sea. Something had to be done to try and resolve the problems that had arisen. The United Nations Conference on the Laws of the Sea (UNCLOS) was set up in 1973 as a means of settling ownership of the sea in a peaceful manner. UNCLOS has made the proposal that the ocean should be divided into five types of area:

1) Territorial sea: This extends for 19 km and replaces the old three-mile (4.8 km) limit.

2) Contiguous zone: This extends over a further 38 km over which a country has limited control.

3) Exclusive Economic Zone (EEZ): The country has control over the economic activities such as fishing and mining for 320 km from the shore. Where the distance between countries is less than 640 km, the dividing line is drawn midway between them.

4) Beyond the EEZ are the free high seas, although the ocean bed that extends over the continental shelf can be explored and exploited by the neighbouring country.

5) The rest of the ocean, about 60 per cent, is the 'common heritage of all mankind'. UNCLOS has recommended that an International Sea-bed Authority should be set up to control the mining of the sea-bed for the benefit of all people. One of its first tasks would be to sort out claims from various countries wanting to mine manganese nodules.

The outlook

The oceans are one huge ecosystem and what happens in one part will eventually influence all of it. Pollution that enters the sea is spread over considerable distances by the ocean currents. Many creatures migrate thousands of kilometres through or over the ocean and they are dependent upon the food that the ocean supplies wherever they are.

At the moment, the coastal stretches of the seas are the worst affected by human activity. The deep oceans remain relatively healthy, but there must be more sensible control of their resources if they are to remain so.

The UNEP Regional Seas Programme is bringing countries together and helping them work towards cleaning up their coastal seas. To conserve fish stocks, sensible quotas must be set and agreed by individual countries. The fishing commissions and advisory bodies are the means of doing this.

As a source of raw materials and energy, the oceans are likely to become more important in the future, but the question of who should benefit from their exploitation needs to be resolved. The UNCLOS proposals for dividing up the ocean have not yet been agreed by any country.

Finding a means of conserving the oceans is a major challenge for the world community. It will require levels of international co-operation that humans have never achieved before. Marine conservation will be a symbol of how well we can expect to deal with other environmental issues. If we can co-operate and manage the oceans sensibly, then we will have shown that humans can solve global environmental problems. There is then a very good chance of solving all the other environmental problems that face life on Earth.

You have read that some marine conservation campaigns have been very successful — for example, the campaign to prevent whaling. Environmental organizations such as Greenpeace have successfully drawn international attention to marine pollution problems. You can play your part in protecting the oceans by learning as much as you can about ocean life and by joining a conservation society. Some useful addresses are given on page 47.

'We can no longer use the world's ocean as a dustbin. We must view it as a living ecosystem, a vital and integral part of our planet's workings'.

The crew of the Greenpeace ship Rainbow Warrior.

Rainbow Warrior *was the boat used by Greenpeace to draw attention to activities that damaged the marine environment. It was sunk in 1987, apparently by agents of the French government, prior to a series of French nuclear tests in the Pacific Ocean.*

Glossary

Cetaceans The name given to sea mammals which have no hind limbs and breathe through a blow hole. They include whales, porpoises and dolphins.
Continental shelf The part of a continent that continues under the sea.
Convention An agreement made by a group of countries to work together towards a common goal.
Ecology The study of how plants, animals and the environment in which they live affect one another.
Ecosystem A self-contained group of plants and animals and the environment in which they live.
Environment The surroundings in which plants and animals live (marine environment refers to the sea, terrestrial environment to the land).
Exclusive Economic Zone The area of sea surrounding a country over which it can control economic activities like fishing and mining. The zone extends 320 km out from the coast.
Habitat The natural home of particular plants and animals.
Inorganic A substance not related to living plants or animals, for example rocks.
Migrate To travel from one part of the world to another.
Moratorium A total ban.
Nature reserve A habitat that is protected from activities that might damage it.
Organic A substance that is derived from living material.
PCBs A group of human-made chemicals used in plastics, the electrical industry and hydraulic fluids. They are very toxic and are not broken up by nature.
Pollutants Substances which when released into the environment can cause damage to it.
Pollution The presence of harmful substances called pollutants in the environment.
Quota A permitted set quantity.
Radioactivity The radiation given off by certain materials, especially those used in the nuclear industry.
Sewage Waste matter from homes and factories that goes either to a sewage treatment plant or direct into rivers or the sea.
United Nations The international organization that brings governments of countries together to discuss and attempt to solve world problems.

Picture acknowledgements

The photographs in this book are reproduced by kind permission of: Bruce Coleman Ltd 8 above, 10 (Lanting), 11 above (Ziesler), 21 (Hughes), 22 above (Hans Reinhard), 25 (Bingham), 26 above (Cubitt), 29 (Townsend) , 33 (Everson), 34 (Alexander), 35 above (Boulton), 39 above (Dore), 40 above (Compost), 41 below (Roessler), . Greenpeace 20 (Gleizes). Hutchison Library 44 (Hall). Natural Science Photos 42 (Ken Cole). Oxford Scientific Films 6 (Sandved), 8 below (Hauser), 9 (Zell), 11 below, 16 and 45 (Westerskov), 13, 23 and 38 (Toms), 15 (Lockwood), 19 (Cayless), 24 above (Birkhead), 26 below (Parks), 28 (Perrins), 30, 35 below (Merlen), 36 and 37 above (Martin), 39 below (Walsh), 41 above (Leszczynski), 42 above. Rex Features 27 above (Orth), and below (Today). Paul Seheult 22 (below). ZEFA *Cover,* 4, 7 (W Townsend Jnr), 12 (James), 17 (Boutin), 24 below, 31 (Moloney), 32 (Bingel), 37 below (Ferchland), 40 below.The illustrations are by Marilyn Clay on pages 4–5, 13 and 14, and by Stephen Wheele on page 18.

Further reading

Coastline: Britain's Threatened Heritage (Kingfisher Books, 1987)
The Dying Sea Michael Bright (Franklin Watts, 1988)
Finding Out About the Coast John Bentley and Bill Charlton (Batsford, 1985)
Gaia Atlas of Planet Management (Pan, 1985)
Ocean Life David Cook (Hamish Hamilton, 1983)
Oceans Martin Bramwell (Franklin Watts, 1984)
Oceans and Seas Terry Jennings (Oxford University Press, 1988)
The Sea (My First Library Series) (Macdonald, 1986)
Sea Pollution (wallchart) Pictorial Charts Educational Trust
Seas and Oceans David Lambert (Wayland, 1987)
The Times Atlas of the Oceans (Times Books, 1983)
Waste and Recycling Barbara James (Wayland, 1989)
Water Ecology Jennifer Cochrane (Wayland, 1986)
The World's Oceans Cass R Sandak (Franklin Watts, 1987)

Useful addresses

Atlantic Center for the Environment
39 South Main Street
Ipswich
Massachusetts
09138-2321 USA

Australian Conservation Foundation
6726 Glenferrie Road
Hawthorn
Victoria 3122
Australia

Coastwatch UK
Farnborough College of Technology
Boundary Road
Farnborough
Hampshire GU14 6SB

Environment and Conservation Organizations of New Zealand
PO Box 11057
Wellington
New Zealand

Friends of the Earth (UK)
26-28 Underwood Street
London N1 7JQ

Friends of the Earth (USA)
1045 Sansome Street
San Francisco
California CA 94111

Greenpeace (UK)
30-31 Islington Street
London N1 7JQ

Greenpeace (Australia)
310 Angas Street
Adelaide 5000

Greenpeace (Canada)
427 Bloor Street West
Toronto
Ontario

Greenpeace (New Zealand)
Private Bag
Wellesley Street
Auckland

Marine Conservation Society (UK)
4 Gloucester Road
Ross-on-Wye
Herefordshire HR9 5BU

Index